My Cat is in LOVE with the GOLDFiSH

AND OTHER LOOPY LOVE POEMS

Chosen by Graham Denton

Illustrated by Nigel Baines

A & C Black • London

For Mum and Dad, Alison, and Clare,
with lots of loopy love – Graham

With thanks to Bernard Young for the original poem
that inspired the title of this collection

First published 2010 by
A & C Black Publishers Ltd
36 Soho Square, London, W1D 3QY

www.acblack.com

ISBN 978-1-4081-1559-6

A CIP catalogue for this book is available from the British Library.

This book is produced using paper that is made from wood
grown in managed, sustainable forests. It is natural, renewable
and recyclable. The logging and manufacturing processes conform
to the environmental regulations of the country of origin.

Printed and bound in Great Britain
by CPI Cox and Wyman, Reading, RG1 8EX.

Contents

Doomed Love

A Perfect Match

The Food of Love

Animal Magnetism

My Cat Is in Love
with the Goldfish

My cat is in love with the goldfish.
He's practically head over heels.
He cannot hold back his emotions
or mask the affection he feels.

He'll bring her big bundles of roses.
He'll give her these syrupy notes
declaring undying devotion,
embellished with cute little quotes.

He'll pen the most passionate poems
a pussy could possibly write,
then sit by her bowl in the evening
and promptly proceed to recite.

He'll whisper such sickly sweet nothings
whilst barely averting his gaze.
He'll sing serenades in her honour,
whose verses are bursting with praise.

Yes, my cat's so in love with the goldfish,
yet the chances of romance are poor,
for, alas, the attraction's one-sided...
the fish loves the tabby next door!

Graham Denton

Under the Apple Tree

As I sat under the apple tree,
A birdie sent his love to me,
And as I wiped it from my eye,
I said, "Thank goodness cows can't fly."

Anon

The Owl and the Pussycat

The owl and the pussycat
Went to sea
The owl ate the pussycat
Oh, deary me

Roger Stevens

The Spider and the Fly

Said the spider to the fly
"You're a funny little guy –

yet I find I love you so."
"So set me free," said Fly. "Oh no!"

said Spider. "Here is fine.
Let's relax and soon we'll dine."

"Dine?" said Fly. "There's no food here!"
Spider grinned. "It's you, my dear."

James Carter

Last Waltz

Solo was a Dodo
the last one in the land.
She didn't go to parties
or dance to birdland bands.
She hadn't got a partner,
she hadn't got a friend,
until –

　　　she met a Panda,
　　　a Pandaman called Ben.

Will you dance with me? asked Solo
Can we be a party pair?

Will you take a sprig of blossom
       – will you weave it in my hair?
Will you hold me very tightly?
        – can I hold you to my breast?
        – can I snuggle really closely
           upon your hairy chest?

The woodland flutes played softly,
the evening sang its charms
      to a Panda dancing slowly
         with a Dodo
         in its arms.

Peter Dixon

I Wish I Had Your Picture...

I wish I had your picture –
It would be very nice.
I'd hang it in the attic
To scare away the mice.

Anon

Advice to a Heartbroken Shark

When Sharon the shark split up with him
Shaun didn't understand.
But his best friends tried to cheer him up
"There's plenty more folk on the land!"

Paul Cookson

A Lobster Wooed a Lady Crab

A lobster wooed a lady crab,
And kissed her lovely face.
"Upon my sole," the crabbess cried,
"I wish you'd mind your plaice!"

Anon

The Skunk and the Porcupine

A skunk fell in love with a porcupine;
they married and had a baby.
I think that they called it a skunkupine,
or was it a porcuskunk, maybe?

Perhaps it was really a punkuskine,
or maybe a pinyskorkpunk.
There's only one thing that's for certain –
it felt like a cactus and stunk.

Kenn Nesbitt

I Love You, I Love You, I Love You, I Do...

I love you, I love you, I love you, I do.
Don't get so excited, I love monkeys, too!

Anon

Pig's Song of Courtship

Grobble   Snort
Blurp   Blort
Screep   Uggle
Slop   Snuffle
Honk   Squelch
Flubber   Belch
Wee   Say
Wee   You
Wee   Love
Wee   Me

John Mole

Snout Doing

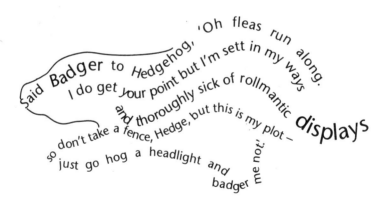

Said Hedgehog to Badger, 'Oh, let's matty do -
We'll shickle and bruffle and sup hogger stew
We'll insect each other with liCe evermore,
have badgehogs in batches and hedgers galore.
we'll live till we snuffit twogether as one.'

Said Badger to Hedgehog, 'Oh fleas run along.
I do get your point but I'm sett in my ways
and thoroughly sick of rollmantic displays
so don't take a fence, Hedge, but this is my plot -
just go hog a headlight and badger me not.'

Gina Douthwaite

The Stuff of Fairy Tales

Jack and June

Jack and June went to the moon,
Crash-landed in a crater.
Jack broke his nose and seven toes.
(He's a crummy navigator!)

Jack cried in pain. June tried in vain
To soothe her injured mate.
She bound his toes and kissed his nose
And asked him for a date.

Jack and June began to swoon…
Fell mad in love, and they
Returned to Earth, their place of birth…
And wed the very next day.

Elaine Magliaro

Lonely Heart

Handsome, lean wolf
Likes acting and cooking
Tired of old grannies
Is currently looking
For lady in red
With plump and soft skin
To share walks in the forest
And cosy nights in

Rachel Rooney

Letters from Beauty

Dear Daddy, I'm so lonely.
I'm living with a Beast –
It's true he owns a castle
Where EVERY meal's a feast,
But shadows in the mirror
Are full of gloom and sorrow...
PLEASE come and save your daughter
And take me home tomorrow.

Dear Dad, Perhaps my letter
Has somehow gone astray.
I'm STILL inside this palace,
I'm STILL locked up all day.
The Beast is creeping closer,
I hear him snort and roar...
Please take me home TOMORROW
(As I have asked before).

Dear Father, STILL no answer,
No sign of help at all.
The Beast is big and grumpy,
He prowls around the hall,
He growls around the garden,
He dribbles when he chews...
Please take me home THIS MINUTE,
Before I'm next week's news.

Dear Sir, It's been a fortnight
Since first I sent a note.
It's time you gave the answer
To all the things I wrote.
The Beast is keen on dancing,
He likes to twirl and bow,
He spins me round the bathroom…
Please take me home RIGHT NOW!

Dear Daddy, Scrap the rescue,
Don't try to set me free,
I kissed the Beast last Thursday
And we're happy as can be.
My fangs are sharp and spiky,
My fur is green and blue,
And Beasty seems quite handsome
Now I'm a monster too… xxxxx

Clare Bevan

All Mixed Up

Once a mermaid quite riddled with doubt,
Used to sit on the rocks, and would pout.
For she half loved a sailor,
Named Augustus P. Taylor,
But her other half fancied a trout.

Robert Scotellaro

Dragon Love Poem

when you smile
the room lights up

and I have to call
the fire brigade

Roger Stevens

Rapunzel! Rapunzel!

"Rapunzel! Rapunzel! You've cut off your hair!
Your billowing tresses are no longer there.
That mohawk you're sporting is spiky and pink.
I'm really not certain just what I should think.

"I came here expecting to clamber a braid,
ascending your tower to come to your aid.
Instead I have suffered the greatest of shocks
to find that you've cut off your lovely blonde
   locks."

"Prince Charming, Prince Charming,"
  Rapunzel replied.
"I have no intention of being your bride.
We will not get married. We will not elope.
I've cut off my hair and I've braided a rope.

"You came here to visit me once every day,
and promised that soon you would take
  me away,
but you were too clueless to even conceive
of cutting my hair off so we could just leave.

"I cannot believe you were such a big dope.
I come and I go as I please with my rope.
And so, I'm afraid I can't give you my hand.
In spite of the fabulous wedding you planned."

From then on Rapunzel was known through
the land.
She toured the world in a rock-and-roll band.
And silly Prince Charming, with rocks in his
head,
rode off and got married to Snow White
instead.

Kenn Nesbitt

A Dark-haired Young Princess

A dark-haired young princess was fond
Of kissing a frog in the pond.
But it made the frog wince
'Cos he wasn't a prince,
And besides, he wanted a blonde.

Mike Jubb

Handsome Prince

"Go on, kiss her,
handsome prince, don't treat it like a duty!
What man wouldn't envy you
for kissing Sleeping Beauty?"

"I'm sorry, but I can't,"
the handsome prince said, eyes a-twinkle.
"My heart, my soul and waking kiss
belong to Rip Van Winkle."

JonArno Lawson

Jack Sprat

Jack Sprat got really fat.
His wife stayed slim and trim.
Perhaps if she'd predicted that,
she'd not have married him.

Linda Knaus

Doomed Love

Opposites Attract

Ice-cube Boy and Fire Girl
both fell in love at school.
Ice-cube Boy thought she was hot,
and she thought he was cool.
But when they tried to hug and kiss
her flame went "fizzle!", "pop!" and "hiss!"
and Ice-cube Boy was turned to steam,
evaporating with a scream.
Their parents cried, "Our son!", "Our daughter!"
"Nothing more than smoke and water,
Now it's clear, it's just a fact –
opposites should *not* attract!"

Paul Hughes

Deadly Affectionate

I love you but
We must not meet –
To do so, I'm not willin';
For I am
Just a little germ
And you are
Penicillin.

Trevor Harvey

Don't Say It with Flowers

My love is like a red, red rose –
She just keeps getting up my nose.
I love her but I'll have to leave her…
I suffer from – *ATCHOO!* – hay fever!

Graham Denton

Saint Valentine's Day Massacre

What did I ever do to Dorothy Prewitt?
She's sent me a heart with an arrow right
   through it!
So ... if she wants war (well, I didn't begin it)
I'll draw her a heart with an axe buried in it!

Philip Waddell

The Tortoise and the Gecko

A gecko sat crying alone by a canyon
with no one beside him. No friend or companion.
When slowly a tortoise came wandering by
and watched as the gecko would sniffle and cry.
He said in a voice that was ancient and frail,
"My dear little lizard, please tell me your tale."

The sad little gecko looked up in surprise,
and, wiping the tears from his round little eyes,
he said to the tortoise, "Please sit for a spell.
My story is nearly too painful to tell.
The gecko I love but I never have seen
is patiently waiting across this ravine.

"I'm sure she's as lovely as lilies in June.
A fine, freckled gecko with eyes like the moon.
I come every morning to sit at the ledge
and shout to my sweetheart this passionate pledge.
'I love you, my darling!' I proudly proclaim,
and soon my beloved, she answers the same."

The heartbroken gecko announced through his tears,
"This long-distance romance has lasted for years."
"A mighty sad story," the old tortoise said
and walked away slowly while shaking his head,
for, try as he might, he could not tell the gecko
he'd fallen in love with the sound of his echo.

Eric Ode

A Tree Toad Loved
a She-toad

A tree toad loved a she-toad
Who lived up a tree.
She was a three-toed tree toad
But a two-toed toad was he.
The two-toed toad tried to win
The she-toad's friendly nod,
For the two-toed tree toad loved the ground
That the three-toed tree toad trod.
But the two-toed tree toad tried in vain.
He couldn't please her whim.
From her tree-toad bower
With her three-toed power
The she-toad vetoed him.

Anon

It's Not the Real Thing

For robots I feel sympathetic,
Their love is not real – it's synthetic!
Though the tin groom and bride
Do stick close side by side,
Their attraction is merely magnetic.

Philip Waddell

There Was a Young Woman

There was a young woman
who lived in a shoe
for the man that she married
was not well to do.
The woman eventually filed a suit –
She got the shoe, and he got the boot.

Linda Knaus

Doomed Love

It was the talk of seven oceans
The affair that might have been
When the whale fell head over tail in love
With a submarine.

Roger Stevens

Love's Labour Lost

A dinosaur sat by a giant fern,
In a mood of rapt reflection.
He wished to convey what he had to say
To the object of his affection.

So with a claw he began to score,
On a rock, a very large 'kiss',
And then there flowed a true-love ode,
That went … something like this:

Shall I compare thee to a volcano
That roars and shakes the earth?
And how can the mightiest of mountains reflect
Your amplitudinous girth?

Like sun-bleached bones on the desert shine,
I'm reminded of your teeth.
Your bright-red maw, your blood-dripping jaw
Jutting wonderfully underneath.

Your eyes shining bright like two moons at night
Are so beautiful, I think,
And across the ground for miles around
Is the loveliness of your stink.

Say you'll be mine. Then I'll be yours,
The happiest there's ever been.
Yes, I will be your Tyrannosaurus Rex,
And you my Tyrant Queen.

We cannot tell if she loved him well
As he roared his poem, verbatim.
Because, alas, when he got to line ten,
She turned around and ate him.

MORAL:

When in love, you just might think
Your sweetheart is a stunner.
But read her dodgy poetry...?
Be prepared to do a runner!

Ian Larmont

A Conversation in Eden

My darling Eve, my perfect mate,
the night is young. How 'bout a date?
Our lives could use a little spice.
It's boring here in Paradise.
I'm sick of naming snakes and slugs
and snails and quails and ladybugs.
This garden's driving me insane.
It's time we raised a little Cain.

Oh, Adam, honey, not tonight.
I'm sure I look an awful sight.
I have to wash and dry my hair.
I haven't got a thing to wear.
And worse, I've got this aching head.
Let's spend the night at home instead.
A quiet dinner, you and I.
And for dessert, there's apple pie.

Eric Ode

A Perfect Match

On the Very First Valentine's Day

What the caveman gave his missus –
Lots and lots of *Ughs* and kisses!

Graham Denton

If I Were X

If I were x
And you
Were y,
I'd stand
By you
And ... multiply
And once
The two
Of us
Were paired,
Why, they
Would call us
$(xy)^2$

J. Patrick Lewis

Geo-met-Trish

Two lonely squares
met on the corner
and decided to
get oblong together.

Trevor Millum

Attraction

You came and leaned over to see what I drew:
The pictures don't matter; my pencil drew you.

Celia Warren

Love Has an Effect on Our Teacher

When our teacher fell in love with a doctor
She was ill every day of the week
When she fell in love with a plumber
Her radiator sprang a leak
When she fell in love with a dustman
She put her bin out every day
When she fell in love with a farmer
She spent the weekends baling hay
When she fell for a librarian
She was always borrowing books
When she fell in love with a policeman
She went chasing after crooks
But when another teacher
Took our teacher's attention
They got married straight away
And kept each other in detention.

John Coldwell

Sheila Shorter Sought a Suitor

Sheila Shorter sought a suitor;
Sheila sought a suitor sort.
Sheila's suitor's sure to suit her;
Short's the suitor Sheila sought!

Anon

A Perfect Match

A match from heaven
we must be.
You think I'm amazing,
and I agree.

Eric Ode

A Whole Lotto Love

I love you more than all the tea in China.
I love you more than words can ever say.
And ever since your parents won the Lotto
I've loved you more and more with every day!

Graham Denton

My Heart Flies

I love you, Miss Fly.
You're filthy, that's why.
You're covered in grease, dirt and grime.
I gasp at your beauty,
my dung-munching cutie;
and pray that one day you'll be mine.

Let's fly to a pile
of garbage so vile –
it makes quite the loveliest food.
We'll feast there for days
and together we'll raise
a horrible, maggoty brood!

Paul Hughes

An Ode to Keith, My Old Guitar

Listen up
my 6-string
chum...for
you're
the
rea
-son
that
I
strum
...and
pick
and
plunk
and
have
the
funk.
Keith: you
are my #1.
You're brown. You're
wood. You're round. That's...
good. You're thin. You're wide.
You've...dust inside. You're
where I go, when I feel low.
You help me lose
the blues you know. You
rock...you roll. You're folk
(with soul). And yes, you swing,
you crazy thing. You jingle,
jangle. And you twang.
You're *my guitar.*
I'm so *YOUR*
FAN.

James Carter

The Food of Love

Bread Boy

Bread Boy met Crumpet Girl;
Their relationship couldn't fail.
They got married one summer's day
Before the romance went stale.

But their perfect day was ruined
When they reached the reception room.
The guests all stood and said, "Three Cheers!"
Then toasted the bride and groom.

Chris White

How Passionate!

I know a girl named Passion.
I asked her for a date.
I took her out to dinner
And gosh! How Passion*ate*!

Anon

Hunger Pains

Last night I ate my toenails,
with salt they were delightful.
For brekkie I had scrambled legs,
I cherished every bite-full.
For lunch I nibbled cheese and knees,
and drank a hearty brew.
Then snacked on earlobe custard,
and some earwax in a stew.
Dinner was a handwich
plus a chunky slice of head –

if I eat another morsel
I might be a little dead.

My menu is delicious
but it's vicious to my health.
It's hard to be a cannibal
when you love yourself.

Bill Condon

The Food of Love

I'm in love with my dinner lady
When I see her, my heart skips.
I think she really loves me, too
'Cos she gives me extra chips.

Paul Cookson

The Amorous Teacher's Sonnet to His Love

Each morning I teach in a daze until
the bell that lets me hurry down and queue
with pounding heart to wait for you to fill
my eyes with beauty and my plate with stew.
Dear dinner lady, apple of my eye,
I long to shout I love you through the noise
and take your hand across the shepherd's pie
despite the squealing girls or snickering boys.
O let us flee together and start up
a little café somewhere in the Lakes
and serve day-trippers tea in china cups
and buttered scones on pretty patterned plates.

Alas for dreams so rudely bust in two –
some clumsy child's spilt custard on my shoe.

Dave Calder

My Love Is Like a Cabbage

My love is like a cabbage,
Divided into two –
The leaves I give to others,
The heart I give to you!

Anon

Cupboard Crush

"Tomato, why do you lie there,
Sighing such desperate sighs?
What's wrong?" asks the soft-hearted lettuce,
And the blushing tomato replies:
"I have fallen in love with King Edward –
Those eyes, those eyes, those eyes!"

Richard Edwards

The Dancing Carrot

The beetroot was getting married
The celery squealed with delight
The carrot stood up to dance a jig
And the horseradish whistled all night!

(traditional Czech poem)
translated by Andrew Fusek Peters and
Vera Fusek Peters

Lettuce Marry

Do you carrot all for me?
My heart beets for you,
With your turnip nose
And your radish face.
You are a peach.
If we cantaloupe
Lettuce marry;
Weed make a swell pear.

Anon

Love at First Bite

It all started so well.
I met him in a bar;
He was dark and handsome,
Smooth and rich, too.
I suggested going for a bite;
I held him in my arms,
Our lips touched;
I melted his heart.

That was last week.
He's gone now;
It all went to pieces
(He was a bit of a square).

That's the trouble
When you fall in love
With chocolate.

Andy Seed

Monster
Love

Considerate Monster

It was Valentine's Day, and a monster
  Plucked a bouquet of worms from the
  ground,
Then he added a few snapping lizards
  And smeared them with slime all around.

To the bouquet he added a serpent
  And a branch full of thorns, and a quill,
And included a black-widow spider
  That then weaved a big web for some frill.

He took his fine gift to his ghoulfriend,
  Who was dripping with drool on the stair.
"Oh, Oscar!" she squealed, then embraced
  him.
"It's so nice to know that you care!"

Robert Scotellaro

Valientine

An alien valentine in verse
from elsewhere in the universe.
(Heavens above. It must be love.)

Dear Alien, I love you
with your 13 legs
and your hair so blue
and your beautiful tentacles
covered with goo.

In all of inner or outer space
there cannot be so fair a face
with ears stuck on all over the place.

So let me be your satellite
revolving round you every night.
Tell me, yes. Ah, tell me soon.
For you, my dear, I'm over the moon.

Thinking of you, I cannot sleep.
Yours X-static-ly,
E.T. BLEEP

Tony Mitton

The Alien Wedding

When the aliens got married,
The bride was dressed in zeet;
And with a flumzel in her groyt,
She really looked a treat.

The groom was onggy spoodle,
He felt a little quenz;
The best man told him not to cronk
In front of all their friends.

The bride's ensloshid father
Had slupped down too much glorter;
He grobbled up the aisle alone,
Then flomped back for his daughter.

The lushen bridesmaids followed
With such wigantic walks;
Their optikacious oggers
Were sparkling on their stalks.

The bride and groom entroathed their splice,
They swapped a little squip;
Then he splodged her on the kisser,
And she flimped him on the blip.

And after the wedding breakfast,
The stroadling and the laughter,
The loving pair took off for Mars,
And splayed winkerly ever after.

Mike Jubb

Will You?

Will you be my Valentine?
Will you marry me in June?
Will you lock me in the basement
when there is a bright, full moon?

Will you bring me lots of roses?
Will you bring me chocolate sweets?
Once a month when I get hairy,
will you feed me doggy treats?

Will you treat me with devotion?
Will you bless me when I sneeze?
Will you dust my back with powder
just in case I've gotten fleas?

Will you be my darling angel?
Will you be my dream divine?
That's exactly what the Wolfman
said to Lady Frankenstein

Kenn Nesbitt

Love Letter – from the Wizard to the Witch

I find your looks bewitching,
The way you stand and glare.
I love the way you shake your locks
Of tangled, matted hair.

I find your smile enchanting,
Your wicked, evil grin.
It makes me want to touch and stroke
Your gnarled and wrinkled skin.

I find your face spellbinding,
The warts upon your cheek,
So hairy, black and crusty –
They make my knees go weak.

I find you so enthralling.
I love your witchy smell
Of rats and dung and sewers –
You hold me in your spell!

John Foster

The Vampire's Wedding

For weeks and weeks the town was dreading
the Vampire and the Werewolf's wedding.
The presents were extremely strange –
tooth files and cures for lice and mange,
some rare and vintage blood in vats
and tubs of sugared flies (for bats).

The marriage went off very well.
The vicar flew direct from hell:
he wished them years of endless strife
and then pronounced them bat and wife.

The guests applauded when he sighed,
romantically, "Now, bite the bride!"

According to the best bat's brother,
the new wife ate the bridegroom's mother,
whose husband squeaked, "I don't mind that –
she always was a daft old bat."
Beneath the floodlight of the moon
the Death March played (their favourite tune).

Then with a friendly parting curse
they left the party in a hearse,
tossed out a hellebore bouquet
to little ghouls who lined the way,
and honeymooned with loving mania
for several years in Transylvania.

Marian Swinger and Charles Thomson

Sir Hector

Sir Hector was a spectre
And he loved a lady ghost;
At midnight he'd collect her
And he'd drive her to the coast.

And there upon the shingle
They would rattle all their bones,
And ocean sounds would mingle
With their melancholy moans.

Colin West

Dancing with Frankenstein

Monster Frankenstein thought it was neat
To go dancing with gals that he'd meet,
But the screams quickly came
As they limped off, quite lame,
For he wasn't that light on his feet.

(Or theirs either!)

Robert Scotellaro

Bogeyman's Dilemma

She loves me,
She loves me snot;
She loves me,
She loves me snot...

Andy Seed

Do You Love Me or Do You Not?

Question

Do you love me
Or do you not?
You told me once
But I forgot!

Anon

What to Do if Someone You Really, Really, Really, Really, Really, Really, Really Don't Like Asks You for a Date

Should you get
in such a fix,
simply say:
"1066?"

(Well, they did ask you for a *date*!)

Graham Denton

You Remind Me of the Sea

"You remind me of the sea," he said.
"Deep, untamed and wild."
She sat there, looking modest,
Lovely, meek, and mild.

"What a strange coincidence,"
She answered smooth and slick.
"You remind me of the sea as well –
You always make me sick..."

Clive Webster

Ooh! I Think You're Wonderful

You're the wings on my aeroplane
You're the strings on my guitar
You're the star in my night sky
You're the fuel for my car

You're the answer to my question
You're the pen that writes my line
You're the spring in my onion
You're the tingle down my spine

You're the zipper on my jacket
You're the ketchup on my chips
You're the method in my madness
You're the promise on my lips

You're the headline in my paper
You're all my favourite smells
You're the last piece in my jigsaw
Oops! Sorry, I thought you were someone else

Bernard Young

"Your teeth are like the stars," he said

"Your teeth are like the stars," he said,
And pressed her hand so white.
He spoke the truth, for like the stars,
Her teeth came out at night.

Anon

He and She

To show her how much he loved her
He bought her a beautiful rose,
But it gave her a fit of the sneezes
So she twisted the end of his nose.

To show her how much he loved her
He bought her some Belgian chocs,
But a caramel pulled out her fillings
So she clobbered his head with the box.

To show her how much he loved her
He bought her a basket of pears,
But the one that she bit had a worm in
So she pinched him and kicked him
   downstairs.

So he bought her some yoghurt and treacle,
Which he mixed with cold custard and dirt,
And to show her how much he loved her –
Poured the lot down the front of her shirt.

Richard Edwards

Crossed Lines

Oh, my darling,
oh, my darling,
oh, my darling Clementine...

Please leave your message after the tone.
I'm on the other line...

Oh, my darling,
oh, my darling,
oh, my darling Clementine...

or text me on my mobile phone,
or contact me online...

Oh, my darling,
oh, my darling,
oh, my darling Clementine...

If it's really urgent,
I'll ring back after nine…

Oh, my darling,
oh, my darling,
oh, my darling, darling, darling…

but if it's just a nuisance call,
I'm dialling 999.

Kate Williams

Shoe, Boot! Shoe!

Dear Shoe, I've got
a crush on you,
I think you're
b– o– o– t– i– f– u– l.
Please could you take a
shine to me or do you find me dull?
Dear Boot, you are a silly clog so kindly hold your tongue.
You are a heel and my soft soul, by you, will not be won.
Boot felt his throat tie in a knot. Shoe'd walked all over him!
And now he's stashed back on the shelf,
alone, out on a limb.

Gina Douthwaite

No Great Shakespeare

Shall I compare thee to a summer's day?
You're dull. You're dreary. Now go away!

Graham Denton

Acknowledgements

All poems have been included with kind permission of the authors.

'The Owl and the Pussycat' by Roger Stevens first appeared in *Why Otters Don't Wear Socks* by Roger Stevens, published by Macmillan Children's Books, 2007.

'The Spider and the Fly' by James Carter first appeared in *Hey, Little Bug!: Poems for Little Creatures* by James Carter, published by Hands Up Books, 2007.

'Last Waltz' by Peter Dixon first appeared in *Grand Prix of Poetry* by Peter Dixon, published by Macmillan Children's Books, 1999.

'Advice to a Heartbroken Shark' by Paul Cookson first appeared in *Spill The Beans* by Paul Cookson and David Harmer, published by Macmillan Children's Books, 2000.

'The Skunk and the Porcupine' by Kenn Nesbitt first appeared in *The Aliens Have Landed!* by Kenn Nesbitt, published by Meadowbrook Press, 2001.

'Pig's Song of Courtship' by John Mole first appeared in *The Mad Parrot's Countdown* by John Mole, published by Peterloo Poets, 1990.

'Snout Doing' from *What Shapes an Ape?* by Gina Douthwaite, published by Red Fox. Reprinted by permission of The Random House Group Ltd.

'Lonely Heart' by Rachel Rooney first appeared in *I'm Not Telling You* by Rachel Rooney, published by Rabbit Press, 2004.

'Letters from Beauty' by Clare Bevan first appeared in *A Twist in the Tale*, Poems chosen by Valerie Bloom, published by Macmillan Children's Books, 2005.

'All Mixed Up' and 'Dancing with Frankenstein' by Robert Scotellaro first appeared in *Dancing with Frankenstein and Other Limericks* by Robert Scotellaro, published by Hands Up Books, 2003.

'Dragon Love Poem' by Roger Stevens first appeared in *A Mean Fish Smile* by Roger Stevens, Sue Cowling, and Jan Dean, published by Macmillan Children's Books, 2000.

'Rapunzel! Rapunzel!' by Kenn Nesbitt first appeared in *My Hippo Has the Hiccups: And Other Poems I Totally Made Up* by Kenn Nesbitt, published by Sourcebooks Jabberwocky, 2009.

'A Dark-haired Young Princess' by Mike Jubb first appeared as 'Limerick' in *The Ghost of My Pussycat's Bottom* by Mike Jubb, published by Back to Front, 2006.

'Handsome Prince' by JonArno Lawson first appeared in *Black Stars in a White Night Sky* by JonArno Lawson, published by Pedlar Press, 2006.

'Jack Sprat' and 'There Was a Young Woman' by Linda Knaus first appeared in *Mrs Pringle's Jolly Jingles* by Linda Knaus, published by Hands Up Books, 2006.

'Saint Valentine's Day Massacre' by Philip Waddell first appeared in *Read Me and Laugh*, Selected by Gaby Morgan, published by Macmillan Children's Books, 2005.

'Doomed Love' by Roger Stevens first appeared in *A Sea Creature Ate My Teacher*, Fishy poems chosen by Brian Moses, published by Macmillan Children's Books, 2000.

'Love's Labour Lost' by Ian Larmont first appeared in *The 2nd Beastly Poetry Book* by Ian Larmont, published by Arts Advance Press, 2008.

'If I Were X' by J. Patrick Lewis first appeared in *Poems for Teaching in the Content Areas: 75 Powerful Poems for Enhancing Your History, Geography, Science and Math Lessons* by J. Patrick Lewis and Laura Robb, published by Scholastic Teaching Resources, 2007.

'Love Has an Effect on Our Teacher' by John Coldwell first appeared in *More Secret Lives of Teachers*, Chosen by Brian Moses, published by Macmillan Children's Books, 1997.

'Bread Boy' by Chris White first appeared in *Shark in the Toilet! Potty Poems to Get Your Teeth Into* by Chris White, published by The King's England Press, 2004.

'The Food of Love' by Paul Cookson first appeared in *Crazy Classrooms and Secret Staffrooms* by Paul Cookson, published by Lion Publishing, 2001.

'The Amorous Teacher's Sonnet to His Love' by Dave Calder first appeared in *Dolphins Leap Lampposts* by Dave Calder, Eric Finney, and Ian Souter, published by Macmillan Children's Books, 2002.

'Cupboard Crush' by Richard Edwards first appeared in *The House That Caught a Cold* by Richard Edwards, published by Viking, 1991.

'The Dancing Carrot' translated by Andrew Fusek Peters and Vera Fusek Peters first appeared in *Sheep Don't Go to School*, Edited by Andrew Fusek Peters, published by Bloodaxe, 1996.

'Considerate Monster' by Robert Scotellaro first appeared in *Snail Stampede and Other Poems* by Robert Scotellaro, published by Hands Up Books, 2004.

'Valientine' by Tony Mitton first appeared in *Aliens Stole My Underpants and Other Intergalactic Poems*, Compiled by Brian Moses, published by Macmillan Children's Books, 1998.

'The Alien Wedding' by Mike Jubb first appeared in *Aliens Stole My Underpants and Other Intergalactic Poems*, Compiled by Brian Moses, published by Macmillan Children's Books, 1998.

'Love Letter – from the Wizard to the Witch' by John Foster first appeared in *The Poetry Chest* by John Foster, published by Oxford University Press, 2007.

'The Vampire's Wedding' by Marian Swinger and Charles Thomson first appeared in *Never Say Boo To a Ghost and Other Haunting Rhymes*, Chosen by John Foster, published by Oxford University Press, 1990.

'Sir Hector' by Colin West first appeared in *Not to Be Taken Seriously* by Colin West, published by Hutchinson, 1982.

'You Remind Me of the Sea' by Clive Webster first appeared in *The Hippo Book of Silly Poems*, Compiled by John Foster, published by Scholastic Ltd, 1998.

'He and She' by Richard Edwards first appeared in *Wicked Poems*, Edited by Roger McGough, published by Bloomsbury, 2002.

'Shoe, Boot! Shoe!' from *Picture a Poem* by Gina Douthwaite, published by Hutchinson / Red Fox. Reprinted by permission of The Random House Group Ltd.